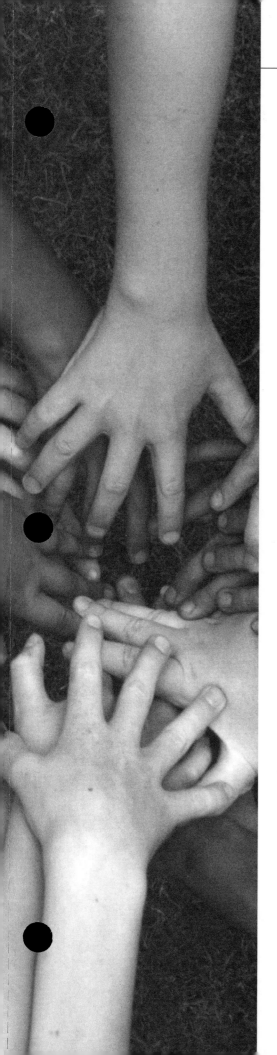

Social Studies Alive!®
My School and Family

TCi™

Chief Executive Officer: Bert Bower

Chief Operating Officer: Amy Larson

Director of Product Development: Liz Russell

Managing Editor: Laura Alavosus

Editorial Project Manager: Lara Fox

Project Editor: Beverly Cory

Editorial Associates: Anna Embree and Sarah Sudano

Production Manager: Lynn Sanchez

Design Manager: Jeff Kelly

Graphic Designer: Cheri DeBusk

Photo Edit Manager: Margee Robinson

Photo Editor: Diane Austin

Art Editor: Sarah Wildfang

Audio Manager: Katy Haun

 Teachers' Curriculum Institute

P.O. Box 50996

Palo Alto, CA 94303

Customer Service: 800-497-6138

www.teachtci.com

ISBN 978-1-58371-782-0

2 3 4 5 6 7 8 9 10 MLI 15 14 13 12 11 10 09

Program Director

Bert Bower

Program Consultant

Vicki LaBoskey, Ph.D., Professor of Education, Mills College, Oakland, California

Student Edition Writers

Laura M. Alavosus

Abigail Boyce

Susan Buckley

Beverly Cory

Wendy Frey

Curriculum Developers

Joyce Bartky

Nicolle Hutchinson

Reading Specialist

Barbara Schubert, Ph.D., Reading Specialist, Saint Mary's College, Moraga, California

Teacher and Content Consultants

Jill Bartky, Teacher, Sharp Park Elementary School, Pacifica, California

Debra Elsen, Teacher, Manchester Elementary, Manchester, Maryland

Gina Frazzini, Literary Coach, Gatzert Elementary, Seattle, Washington

Patrick J. Lee, Teacher, Ohlone Elementary, Palo Alto, California

Jennifer Miley, Teacher, Duveneck Elementary School, Palo Alto, California

Mitch Pascal, Social Studies Specialist, Arlington County Schools, Arlington, Virginia

Jodi Perraud, Teacher, Boulevard Heights Elementary, Hollywood, Florida

Becky Suthers, Retired Teacher, Stephen F. Austin Elementary, Weatherford, Texas

Literature Consultant

Regina M. Rees, Ph.D., Assistant Professor, Beeghly College of Education, Youngstown State University, Youngstown, Ohio

Music Specialist

Beth Yankee, Teacher, The Woodward School for Technology and Research, Kalamazoo, Michigan

Maps

Mapping Specialists, Ltd. Madison, Wisconsin

Contents

Two Goats on a Bridge
A Russian Folk Tale

Once two goats met in the middle of a narrow bridge. The bridge was far too narrow for them to pass.

"Get out of my way!" said one goat. "I want to cross this bridge."

"No, YOU get out of MY way," said the other goat. "I am crossing the bridge. I started first."

Neither goat would back up. But neither goat could go forward, either.

(Stop here for discussion.)

The two goats glared at each other. Then they lowered their heads and began to push each other with their horns.

Both goats were very strong. Neither one could push the other back. But the two goats pushed, and pushed, and pushed *so hard* that they both fell from the bridge and landed in the river.

Wet and angry, both goats stomped home, and neither one got across the bridge.

The Getting Along Song

How can we get along, get along, get along?
How can we get along, get along in school?

I can share my things (share!).
I can share my things (share!).
I can share my things with you.

I can talk to you (talk!).
I can talk to you (talk!).
I can talk to you about my feelings.

How can we get along, get along, get along?
How can we get along, get along in school?

I can listen (listen!).
I can listen (listen!).
I can listen to you.

I can take turns (take turns!).
I can take turns (take turns!).
I can take turns with you.

How can we get along, get along, get along?
How can we get along, get along in school?

Chapter 1 Assessment

Big Ideas

Look at the pictures.

1. Which children are taking turns?

   Color them blue.

2. Which children are talking and listening?

   Color them red.

Reading Further

3. Draw a garden to share.

Show You Know

4. What can you do to get along at school?

   Draw a picture.

We Are Special

We are all alike in some ways.
Different in some ways, too.
We are all special.
What makes you special?

We are good at different things.
Some of us are good at drawing,
Counting, or singing.
What makes you special?

What things can you do well?

You can learn from me.
I can help you learn new things.
What would you like to learn from me?

I can learn from you.
You can help me learn new things.
What would you like to help me learn?

Each of us is special.
We are good at different things.
You can learn from me.
I can learn from you.
Special . . . We're special . . . We are all special.

All About Me

Fill in the blank or circle the answer.

My name is _____.

I am _____ years old.

I am a

girl   boy

I like

art   music   talking   athletics

solving problems   make-believe   reading

Draw a picture. Label it.

My favorite thing to do is

Role Cards

✂ ---- ---- ---- ---- ---- ---- ---- ---- ----

I am the talker.

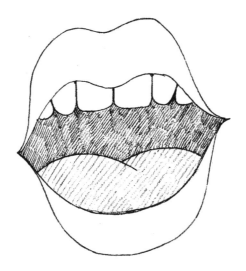

(Fold)

I am the listener.

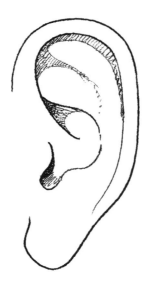

✂ ---- ---- ---- ---- ---- ---- ---- ---- ----

A Gift to Our Class

_____ is a gift to our class.
(name)

Chapter 2 Assessment

Big Ideas

1. Look at the pictures. What can you learn from

   a friend? Draw a circle around it.

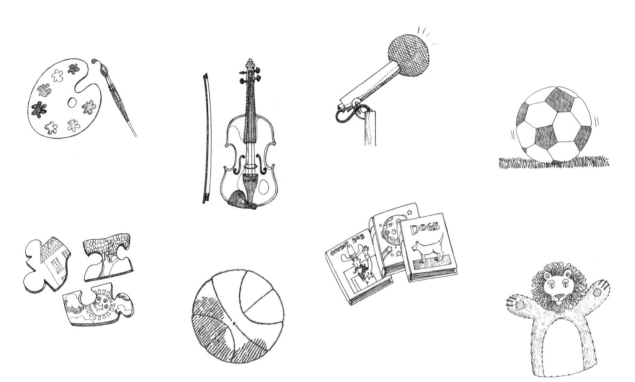

2. Find two things that are alike.

   Color them yellow.

© Teachers' Curriculum Institute

Reading Further

3. Which animal works hard? Color it blue.

Show You Know

4. What makes you special? Draw a picture.

   Show something that you like to do.

Chapter 3 Assessment

Big Ideas

1. Look at the pictures. The children are following rules. Match each picture to the way the rule helps. Draw lines.

Rules

Wear a helmet.

Raise your hand.

Share things.

How Rules Help

Rules help us learn.

Rules help us be fair.

Rules help us be safe.

Why Do Schools Have Rules? **13**

Reading Further

2. Write the missing word on the line.

   The children went to City Hall. They learned how

   people make _____ for their city.

Show You Know

3. Make up a rule to help children get along.

   Write the rule: _____

   _____

   Draw a picture to show the rule.

I Am a Teacher

Hello. My name is Mr. Hayes. I am a first grade teacher at Seacastle Elementary School. I love being a teacher! Let me tell you what I do.

I bet you have already guessed my most important job. That's right! I teach my students all sorts of new things. Every morning, I'm in the classroom by 8 o'clock, ready to greet my students. Some of them give me a "high five" as they come in the room. Can you show me a high five?

We start class right away, because we have a lot to learn. Every day we have lessons in reading and math. I love teaching social studies. I also teach a great science lesson about frogs. Raise your hand if you like frogs as much as I do!

My students really want to do well in school. When they turn in their papers, I check their work. I draw a smiley face on each paper. Can you draw a big smiley face in the air? Then my first graders take the papers home to show their families. Parents always want to know, "How is my child doing in school?" So I talk to moms and dads on the phone, or meet them at school. That's a big part of my job.

It's also my job to make sure my students get along in my classroom. I help them learn the best ways to behave. Do they know how to share and take turns? Do they know how to talk and listen? Do they know the rules? If two students are having problems with each other, we step outside the room. I help them work things out.

I like to help my students learn. I like talking to their families. I like making sure that everyone in my class is happy and safe.

Interview Act-It-Outs

Practice your act-it-out.

Answer these questions:

- Who are you?

- What are you doing?

- How do you help at your school?

I Am a Principal

Hello, girls and boys. My name is Ms. Fortuna. I am the principal at Rosa Parks Elementary School. A principal's job is to be a good leader and make the school a better place. Let me tell you some of the things that I did today.

First thing this morning, a little boy came into the office. He was crying. Can you show me with your face how the boy felt? Yes, he was very sad. I welcomed him into my office and had him sit down. He told me what was wrong. I listened. I was able to give him some good ideas. It's part of my job to help people solve problems. When the boy left my office, he was smiling. Show me with your face how the boy felt now. Yes, he felt much better.

Later in the day, a new family came to see me. I shook hands with them. Can you show me how you would greet a family? The two children were worried about starting class at a new school. I talked to the family. I told them how we would help the children make new friends. As principal, I am always happy to meet with families and talk to them about our school.

After school, I went to a meeting in the teachers' lounge. All the teachers were there. I listened to them. Can you show me how to be a good listener? The teachers told me about the things they needed for their classrooms. That's part of my job, too. I order the books that students use. I keep the supply room stocked with paper. I make sure there are enough glue sticks and paintbrushes for all the classrooms.

I am a good leader at school. I like being a principal because I enjoy helping people, especially kids. I am proud of my school. I want everyone to be proud of our school!

I Am a School Secretary

Hello, children. My name is Ms. Marino, and I am the school secretary at Creative Arts Elementary School. I work in the main office. My job is to help the principal.

I use the phone a lot in my job. I use it to call parents when their children get sick at school. Sometimes families call to leave a message for a teacher, or to speak to the principal. It's my job to make sure that everyone gets their messages. I answer the phone by saying, "Creative Arts School. How can I help you?" Show me how you would answer the phone as a school secretary.

I also use a computer to do my job. I use it to type letters. The letters let families know what is happening at the school. Can you show me how you would type a letter at the computer? I also use the computer to keep track of information. Do you want to know tomorrow's lunch menu? I can look it up in the computer. Do you want to know which day is picture day? Are you wondering when the Book Fair is coming? I can look on a calendar in the computer to find out.

Believe it or not, I couldn't do my job without my smile. When visitors come into the school, I greet them with a smile and help them find the right room. If a girl skins her knee on the playground, I know that a bandage and a smile will help her feel better. Can you show me a big smile?

A school secretary helps people get things done. I greet people, and I help the principal and teachers. My favorite part of my job is helping children. I always have a big smile for them!

Secretary Props

phone

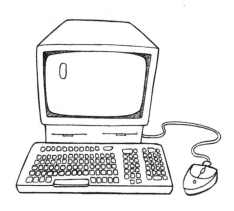

computer

big smile

Talking Statue Act-It-Outs

What will you act out?

Who will be the statue?

How will the statue act?

What will the statue say?

- Tell who you are.

- Tell what you are doing.

- Tell what you do to help at your school.

I Am a School Custodian

Hi. My name is Mr. Harding, and I'm the custodian at Lakeview Elementary School. My job is to make sure everyone at my school is safe and comfortable. Let me tell you a little about my job.

First, I come to school very early, before everyone else. I unlock the front doors so the teachers and children can enter the school. Can you show me how you would turn a key to unlock the doors? Then, I check the temperature to make sure the school isn't too hot or too cold.

During the day, I might fix things—like broken chairs, or a drinking fountain that isn't working. I replace burned out light bulbs. I help people carry heavy things, like boxes full of books. When something needs painting, I bring my paintbrush and go to work.

One thing I love about my job is that I get to work indoors and outdoors. Outside, I raise and lower the flag each day. I mow the grass on the playground. Inside, I help mop up spills. We wouldn't want anyone to slip and get hurt. Can you show me how you would help me mop up some spilled juice? I'm also in charge of the Lost and Found. I can help children find something they've lost, like a jacket.

When everyone else leaves at the end of the day, my job is still not over. I keep working. I vacuum and mop the floors. I take out the trash and the recycling. It's my job to make sure the classrooms are really clean when everyone comes back to school the next day. When my work is done for the day, I lock the doors so everything stays safe. Can you help me lock the doors again?

I help keep the school running smoothly. I really like helping the children and the teachers. It makes me feel proud to keep our school clean and beautiful.

Custodian Props

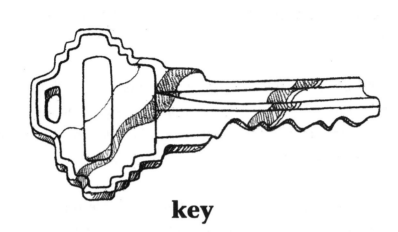

key

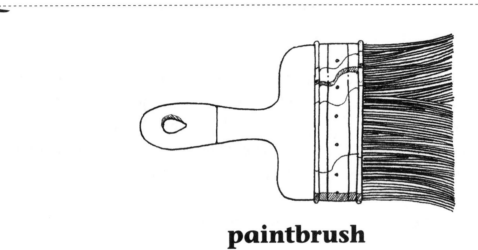

paintbrush

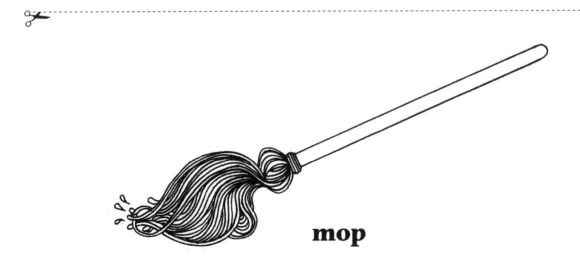

mop

Class Book: How the Teacher Helps Us

Teacher, what do you see?

Class Book: How the Teacher Helps Us

 Teacher, what do you hear?

Class Book: How the Teacher Helps Us

Teacher, what do you touch?

Class Book: How the Principal Helps Us

Principal, what do you see?

Class Book: How the Principal Helps Us

Principal, what do you hear?

Class Book: How the Principal Helps Us

Principal, what do you touch?

Class Book: How the Secretary Helps Us

Secretary, what do you see?

Class Book: How the Secretary Helps Us

Secretary, what do you hear?

Class Book: How the Secretary Helps Us

Secretary, what do you touch?

Class Book: How the Custodian Helps Us

 Custodian, what do you see?

Class Book: How the Custodian Helps Us

 Custodian, what do you hear?

Class Book: How the Custodian Helps Us

 Custodian, what do you touch?

Chapter 4 Assessment

Big Ideas

Look at the pictures.

1. Draw a red circle around the custodian.

2. Draw a blue circle around the principal.

3. Draw a green circle around the secretary.

4. Draw a brown circle around the teacher.

Reading Further

5. Match the leaders to what they lead. Draw lines.

governor   city

mayor   school

president   country

principal   state

Show You Know

6. Draw a picture of someone who helps children at school. Write the name of that person's job.

	Word Bank
	teacher
	principal
	secretary
	custodian

I am a school _____.

Situation 1: Spilled Crayons

Kira drops her crayons on the floor. She asks for help.

What's the best thing to do?

    A   Help Kira pick up the crayons.

    B   Watch Kira pick up the crayons.

    C   Ask the teacher if you can help Kira.

Follow these steps:

    Step 1 Talk about the answers.

    Step 2 Choose the best answer.

    Step 3 Plan an act-it-out about your answer.

    How Are We Good Helpers at School?

Situation 2: Littering

Paula forgets to use the trashcan. You see her throw trash on the floor. What is the best thing to do?

A   Remind Paula to use the trashcan.

B   Pick up the trash and throw it away.

C   Act as if you didn't see what Paula did.

Follow these steps:

Step 1   Talk about the answers.

Step 2   Choose the best answer.

Step 3   Plan an act-it-out about your answer.

© Teachers' Curriculum Institute

Situation 3: New Student in Class

A new girl comes to class.

What is the best thing to do?

A Stare at her.

B Wait for the teacher to introduce her.

C Smile and say hello.

Follow these steps:

Step 1 Talk about the answers.

Step 2 Choose the best answer.

Step 3 Plan an act-it-out about your answer.

Situation 4: Poster Contest

The red group's poster wins the poster contest. Your group's poster doesn't win. What is the best thing to do?

A   Clap for the red group.

B   Try harder next time.

C   Be mean to the red group.

Follow these steps:

Step 1   Talk about the answers.

Step 2   Choose the best answer.

Step 3   Plan an act-it-out about your answer.

Good Helpers

We help others when we're at school.
We can help the teacher clean up the room.
We share books with friends and others, too.
We help each other at our school.

CHORUS:
We help others.
We take care of our things.
We do our best and
Show respect to others.

We take care of our things at school.
We are careful with our paint and glue.
We put our things away when we're through.
We take care of our things at school.

CHORUS

We always do our best at school.
We ask questions we need answers to.
During recess we follow the rules.
We do our best at school.

CHORUS

We respect others at school.
We say "please" and "thank you."
Doesn't matter if we win or lose.
Respect others at school.

CHORUS

Making a Helping Hand Award

1. Who should get a Helping Hand Award?

   Write that person's name at the top of the award.

2. Why should this person get the award?

   Write your answer in the box.

3. Draw a picture.

   Show how the person is a good helper.

4. Decorate and color the award.

Helping Hand Award

has earned a
Helping Hand Award for

Chapter 5 Assessment

Big Ideas

Look at the picture.

1. Find a child who is helping another child learn.

   Draw a circle around them both.

2. Find a child who is putting things away.

   What is being put away? Color those things blue.

Reading Further

3. What did Clara Barton do? Fill in the blank.

She started the American _____ .

Word Bank		
nurses	Red Cross	teachers

Show You Know

4. Think of a way to show respect. Write it on the line.

_____

Draw a picture of it.

Yikes! A Mouse!

Note to Teacher: Phrases in italics are a repeated chorus where students can chime in. Terms in bold type are for your reference during the second reading, indicating where you should pause for placement of the placards as students recreate the classroom "map."

Every day, the children in Ms. Hutchinson's class gathered happily around the two round tables. But one day, the children were scared to enter the classroom. Someone had heard there was a white mouse loose in the classroom! Brave Ms. Hutchinson decided to go in, alone, to look for the mouse.

She opened the **door** and looked around. *No white mouse.* She looked under the **round tables**. *No white mouse.* She carefully opened the doors of the **cabinet** and peered inside. *No white mouse.* She went to her **desk** and looked all around. *No white mouse.* She walked around the **student desks**. *No white mouse.* She carefully, oh so carefully, looked under the balls and jump ropes in the **recess basket**. *No white mouse!*

Finally, she went to the **rectangular table**. She looked on the left side of the **computer**. *No white mouse.* She looked on the right side of the computer. Suddenly, Ms. Hutchinson began to laugh. Next to the white computer, she saw a white computer mouse. There was that white mouse!

Just then, at the back of the room, Ms. Hutchinson heard a little voice. "Squeak! Squeak! Squeak!" said the little voice.

"Yikes!" said Ms. Hutchinson. "A mouse!"

[Stop here during the preview. Read the complete story with the final paragraph during the Social Studies Skill Builder.]

The mouse looked at Ms. Hutchinson. Ms. Hutchinson looked at the mouse. Ms. Hutchinson was scared, but so was the mouse. The mouse was so scared that it ran all the way up the back wall and across the ceiling. Now the mouse was looking down on the classroom from above. What do you think the classroom looked like from up there?

Cutouts of Classroom Objects

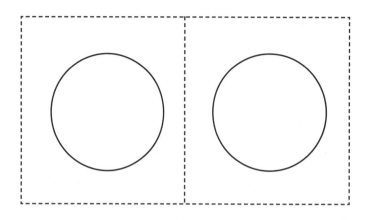

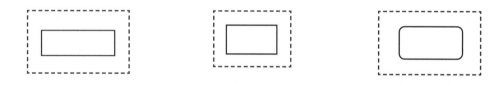

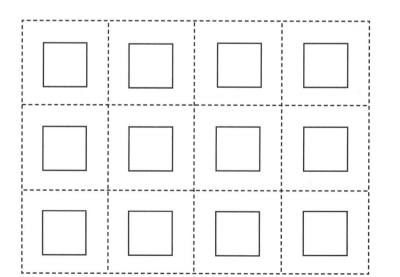

Chapter 6 Assessment

Big Ideas

Read each question. Draw a circle around the best answer.

1. What does a map show?

   a place

   a time

   a story

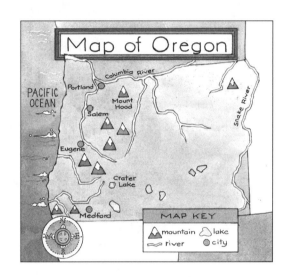

2. This is a compass rose. What does the S on the compass rose mean?

   School

   South

   Sunday

Reading Further

3. Anna wants to walk to the library. She is not sure where it is. Which map should she use? Circle the best answer.

   A. globe   B. state map   C. town map

Show You Know

4. Draw a small map of your classroom. Show:
   - the walls and the door.
   - tables, chairs, or other things.
   - a map key with two symbols.

Cutouts for Mister Bob's Timeline

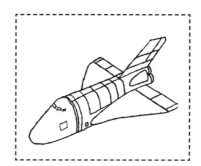

Chapter 7 Assessment

Big Ideas

Look at the pictures of things found in a school.

1. Draw blue circles around things from long ago.

2. Draw red circles around things from today.

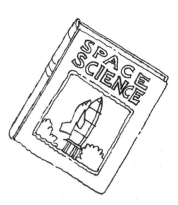

© Teachers' Curriculum Institute

Reading Further

3. Put these in order. Which came first, next, last?

   Label them 1, 2, 3.

Show You Know

4. Draw a classroom from long ago. Show three things

   that are different from your school. Label them.

Word Bank

stove

hornbook

slates

hoops

chalk

desk

Four Family Groups

Four School Groups

Four Community Groups

We Belong to Groups

CHORUS:
We all belong to groups.
School, family, community, too.
We belong to many groups.
What groups do you belong to?

The first group is the one you're in now.
Take a look around and see.
You belong to a school group.

_____

CHORUS

When you go home from school
There are people taking care of you.
You belong to a family group.

_____

CHORUS

There are many community groups.
Soccer and dance are two.
You belong to a community group.

_____

CHORUS

Chapter 8 Assessment

Big Ideas

1. Match the words to the pictures. Draw lines.

school group

family group

community group

Reading Further

2. Naomi is in a special group. Circle the picture that shows what her group makes.

 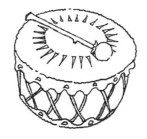 

Show You Know

3. Think of something you do with a group.

   • Draw a picture of your group.

   • What kind of group is it? Fill in the blank.

I am in a _____ group.

Word Bank
community
family
school

My Family Is Special

by _____

My Family Members

The members of my family are

_____

_____

My Family Home

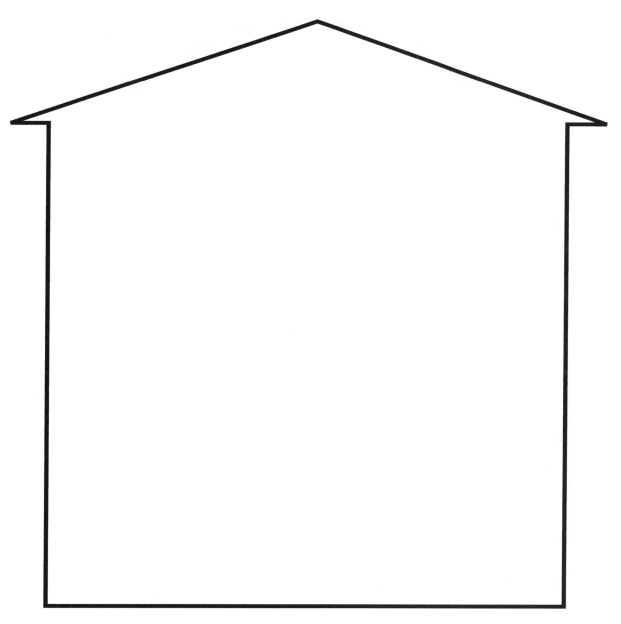

My favorite place at home is

_____

_____

My Family Activities

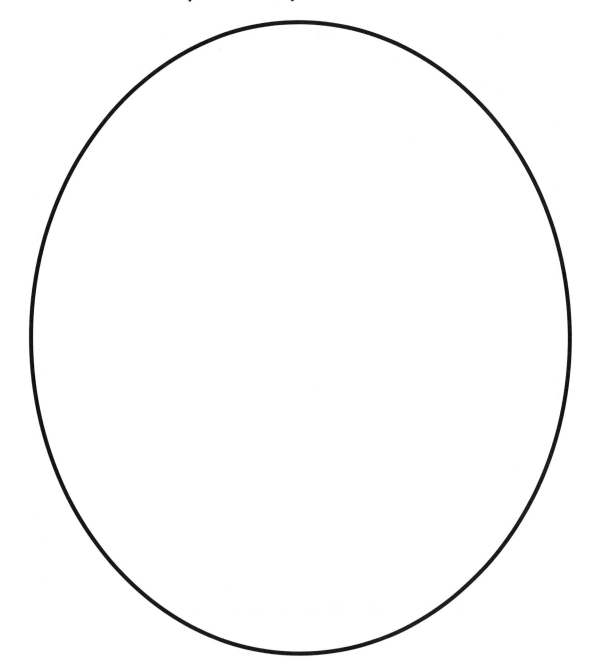

My family likes to

_____

_____

Chapter 9 Assessment

Big Ideas

Look at the pictures.

1. Which picture shows family members?

   Draw a blue circle around the family members.

2. Which picture shows a home?

   Draw a red circle around the home.

Reading Further

3. Fill in the blanks. Use the Word Bank.

I live ————————

————————————.

I live ————————

————————————.

I live ————————

————————————.

Word Bank		
in a city	in a desert	on a farm

Show You Know

4. What activities does your family like? Draw a

   picture. Show your family doing something for fun.

Needs and Wants

CHORUS:
Every family has needs and wants.
Families need basic things.
Food, clothing, shelter
Are what they need to live.
These are the three basic needs.

If a sandwich is a need, pat your head.
If shoes are a need, stomp your feet.
If a house is a need, turn around.

Every family has needs and wants.
Families want many things.
They don't need these things to live
But they make them happy.

If a TV is a want, slap your lap.
If toys are a want, touch your toes.
If popcorn is a want, clap up high.

CHORUS

Bingo Cards

1 Need	1 Want
2 Need	2 Want
3 Need	3 Want
4 Need	4 Want
5 Need	5 Want
6 Need	6 Want
7 Need	7 Want
8 Need	8 Want
9 Need	9 Want

How to Make a Triarama

Materials

construction paper (12-inch squares)

construction-paper scraps

scissors and glue

crayons or markers

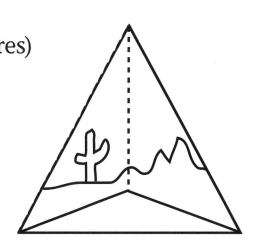

Directions

1. Fold the top right corner of the square down to the lower left corner. Repeat with the top left corner.

2. Open the paper. Cut one fold line to the center of the square.

3. Draw a background scene on half of the square.

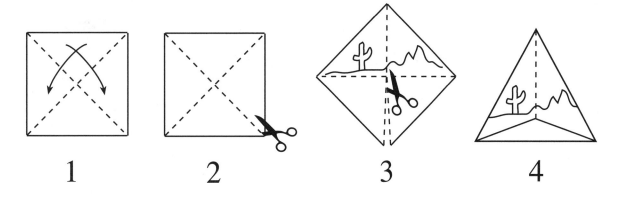

4. Overlap the two bottom triangles, and glue together.

5. To complete the triarama, add cutouts to the scene.

Roles for Your Group

Writer

Writes down the group's choices:

- three food items
- three shelter items
- three clothing items
- three wants

Draws one food need and one want.

Artist

Colors the background.

Draws one clothing need and one want.

Presenter

Draws one shelter need and one want.

Shows the camping triarama

to the class.

Planning a Camping Triarama

Look at your picture. Write the things your group
will need and want.

Food

1. _____

2. _____

3. _____

Clothing

1. _____

2. _____

3. _____

Shelter

1. _____

2. _____

3. _____

Wants

1. _____

2. _____

3. _____

Now circle the things you will draw and cut out

for your camping triarama.

Chapter 10 Assessment

Big Ideas

Look at the pictures.

1. Draw green circles around things that are needs.

2. Draw red circles around things that are wants.

Reading Further

3. Who is working to earn money to meet his family's needs? Draw a circle around him.

Show You Know

4. Think of something your family buys that is a need.

   • Draw a picture.

   • Tell what it is.

My family buys _____.

Family Pictures

Circle 1

Family Members Help Each Other

Circle 2

Family Members Share What They Know

Circle 3

Family Members Spend Time Together

Proclamation Scroll

I, _____ ,

will try to help my family by _____

_____

_____

_____ .

Chapter 11 Assessment

Big Ideas

Look at the families in the picture.

1. Find someone who is helping a family member.

   Draw a blue circle around the helper.

2. Find two people showing each other that they care.

   Draw a red circle around them.

Reading Further

3. Which picture shows a child who is helping

   take care of Earth? Color the picture green.

Show You Know

4. Draw a picture to show how your family spends time

   together. Write a sentence about what you drew.

_____

_____

Families Change

Families change over time.
Families change.
People grow older, yes they do.
Mothers, fathers, and you do, too.

Families change over time.
Families change.
Families grow big and smaller, too.
You can have a new brother,
or your sister moves away to school.

Families change over time.
Families change.
Where families live can sometimes change.
A sibling grows up and can move away.

Families change over time.
Families change.
Families change over time.
Families change.

Ted's Changing Family

Listen carefully to the story. Follow Ted's directions.

Ted's Story

Hi! My name is Ted. This is a picture of my family and me at my birthday party. I'm going to tell you a little about my family. As I do, I'll ask you to guess who everyone in the picture is.

First of all, I have a dad. He cooked the food at my party. Can you find my dad? **Draw a blue circle around my dad.**

My mom was at my party, too. I was born to her and my dad eight years ago today. **Draw another blue circle around my mom.**

My dad was married before he met my mom. He had two kids already, Meg and Sam. They are almost grown up now. They are both really nice, and we have a lot of fun together. Meg made a "Happy Birthday Ted" sign for me. Sam was there, too. **Draw a red circle around Meg and Sam.**

Mom spent a lot of time making sure Brad didn't get too close to the barbecue. Brad is my baby brother. Mom and Dad just adopted him. **Draw a green circle around Brad.**

My grandmother said she wouldn't miss my birthday party for anything in the world. She is my mother's mother. She lives with us. **Draw a blue circle around my grandmother.**

I can't forget my dog, Spot. It is my job to take care of him. **Put your finger on Spot.**

Well, now you've met everyone in my family. My family has grown a lot bigger over the years!

Window to the Future

Cut out each shutter. Glue them on the picture of your family in the future.

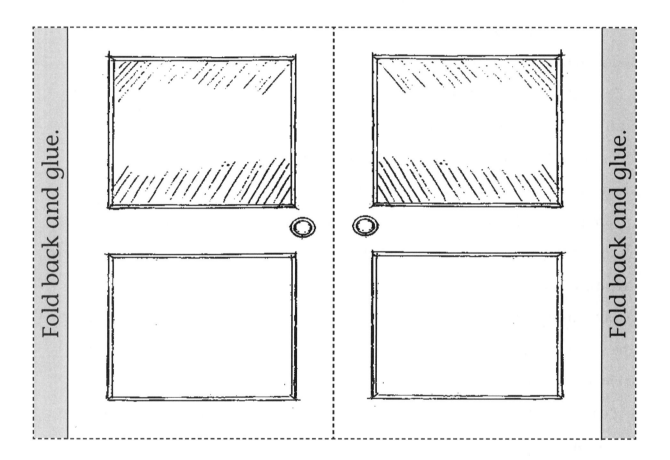

Chapter 12 Assessment

Big Ideas

Draw a line from each sentence to the picture

that is the best match.

1. Families grow

   bigger.

2. Families move to

   new places.

Reading Further

3. What does the picture show? Circle the best answer.

    A. Grandma in the past

    B. Grandma today

    C. Grandma in the future

Show You Know

4. Draw a family that has changed.

    • Show the family before and after the change.

    • What changed? Give your pictures a title.

_____

Tradition Survey

Dear Families,

This week in social studies we are learning about family traditions, or things passed down through the years by family members. They can include food, clothing, music, games, stories, and art.

Please spend a few minutes with your child tonight talking about a celebration that involves your own family traditions. The celebration may relate to a holiday, a birthday, a wedding, or any special occasion your family enjoys. Please help your child complete the survey below. Thank you for your help!

- -

Child's name: _____

Name of your celebration: _____

How do you make this day special?

Food	Clothes
Decorations	Activities (for example: games, songs, stories)

Birthday Party Assignments

Roberto	Mama	Papa	Maria
Thomas	Miguel	Molly	Cristina
Draw decorations	Draw decorations	Draw decorations	Draw decorations
Draw decorations	Draw decorations	Draw decorations	Draw decorations
Draw decorations	Draw decorations	Draw decorations	Draw decorations
Draw food	Draw food	Draw food	Draw food
Draw food	Draw food	Draw food	Draw food
Draw food	Draw food	Draw food	Draw food

Celebrating Special Days

	My Birthday	Roberto's Birthday Party	Chinese Lantern Festival
Decorations			
Food			
Clothing			
Activities			

What Are Family Traditions? **91**

Roberto's Birthday Party

Hola! My name is Roberto Gomez, and I want to tell you about my birthday party. My parents came from Mexico, and my family celebrates birthdays in a special way.

Before my party, Mama and Papa decorated the house with balloons, streamers, and paper flowers.

My sister Maria and I helped set the table. We put out colored plates and napkins. I put on my best jeans and shirt. Maria decided to wear her favorite party dress. Everyone said "Hola!" when they came. They wished me a happy birthday by saying "Feliz cumpleaños" (feh-LEES coom-play-AH-nyohs). Each person also gave me a small present. Of course, I remembered to say "Gracias."

When everyone was there, we ate tacos and tamales. Then we had a special birthday cake. It was round and decorated with whipped cream, flowers, and candles. I made three secret wishes, and then I blew out the candles on top of the cake. Mama cut the cake and gave me the first piece.

After we finished eating, we all gathered around my grandfather. He told us wonderful old stories. We also played games. My favorite game was Coyote and Sheep. It's a little like tag. One person is the coyote and all the rest are sheep. The coyote tries to capture all the sheep to win the game. We were very thirsty after the game, so Mama made us some Mexican lemonade with pineapples, lemons, and cinnamon. It was delicious!

Finally, it was time for the piñata. My friends and I took turns wearing a blindfold and trying to hit the piñata with a stick. It was hard because Papa moved the piñata up and down by pulling on the rope. We all laughed because people looked so funny. We were swinging the stick and just hitting empty air. We kept calling out, telling each other where to swing. I was the one who finally broke the piñata. We all cheered and ran to pick up the treats that scattered all over. It was the best birthday party I ever had.

Play for Roberto's Birthday Party

Characters:

Roberto Gomez

Papa (Roberto's father)

Mama (Roberto's mother)

Maria (Roberto's sister)

Thomas, Miguel, Molly, and Cristina (Roberto's friends)

Narrator: Roberto is having a birthday party. His parents are from Mexico, so his family likes to celebrate in a special way, the same way they did in Mexico. His mama and papa have made special food and decorated the yard. Roberto and Maria tell their friends about the special decorations.

Roberto says _____

Maria says _____

Narrator: Roberto's mama and papa tell everyone about the special food.

Mama says _____

Papa says _____

Narrator: It is time for the piñata. Thomas goes first. He puts on the blindfold and tries to hit the piñata with a stick. Everyone laughs and calls out ways to help him.

Molly says _____

Miguel says _____

Cristina says _____

Roberto says _____

Narrator: Now it's Roberto's turn. He swings the stick. He hits the piñata on his first try. It breaks! Everyone cheers. They pick up the treats that have scattered all over.

Narrator: It is time for dessert. Mama brings out a beautiful birthday cake. Maria reminds Roberto what to do before he blows out the candles.

Maria says _____

Narrator: Everyone sings a birthday song.

The entire class sings "Happy Birthday to You."

Narrator: Finally, it is time for Roberto's friends to leave. As they go,

Molly says _____

Miguel says _____

Thomas says _____

Cristina says _____

Maria says _____

Mama says _____

Papa says _____

Roberto says _____

Dragon Headband

Cut a strip of tag board 18 inches long and 2 inches wide. Tape the ends together to form a child-sized headband. Color and cut out the dragon head below. Glue the dragon head to the front of the headband.

What Are Family Traditions?   **95**

Chinese Lantern Festival

Hello! My name is Alice Chang. I live in San Francisco, California. My family is Chinese American. I'm going to tell you about my favorite Chinese celebration. Chinese New Year celebrations last for many days. People hang lighted lanterns on their front porches, in their gardens, and along the streets. On the last day, we have the Lantern Festival.

Hanging up colored lanterns is an old tradition in China. People would hang lanterns to tell everyone about important events. They hung up red lanterns to tell about happy events, like a new baby or a wedding. They hung up blue lanterns for sad events, like an illness. Of course we hang red lanterns for the New Year. We usually hang one lantern for each person in the family. The lanterns are made of paper or colored glass. Some look like balls or boxes. Others are shaped like animals, cars, and even airplanes.

A few children wear traditional Chinese clothes for the Lantern Festival. I usually wear my prettiest party clothes.

I usually eat so much during the holidays that I'm ready to burst. I love the Chinese dumplings my mom cooks. Dumplings are made of dough that is filled with meat or something sweet. My grandma always hides a coin inside one dumpling. We say that the person who finds the coin will have good luck all year.

On the night of the Lantern Festival, everyone goes out to the street. We watch acrobats, jugglers, and people walking on stilts. My friends and I play hide-and-seek and a game called Catch the Dragon's Tail. But everyone is waiting for the dragon dance.

Finally, it is time. We hear the drums, gongs, cymbals, and firecrackers. We see a parade of people, all carrying lighted lanterns. The best part is when the dragon comes dancing down the street. Lots of dancers are needed to make the dragon move. A person in front of the dragon carries a red or yellow ball on a stick. The ball is supposed to be the sun, and the dragon is chasing it.

The parade ends with firecrackers. They're really loud! Everyone feels tired but happy. We all know we will have lots of good luck in the coming year.

Traditions Quilt Square

 1. Find the diamond. Draw a picture of your family there.

2. Find the triangles. Draw the decorations, food, clothes, and activities for your special day.

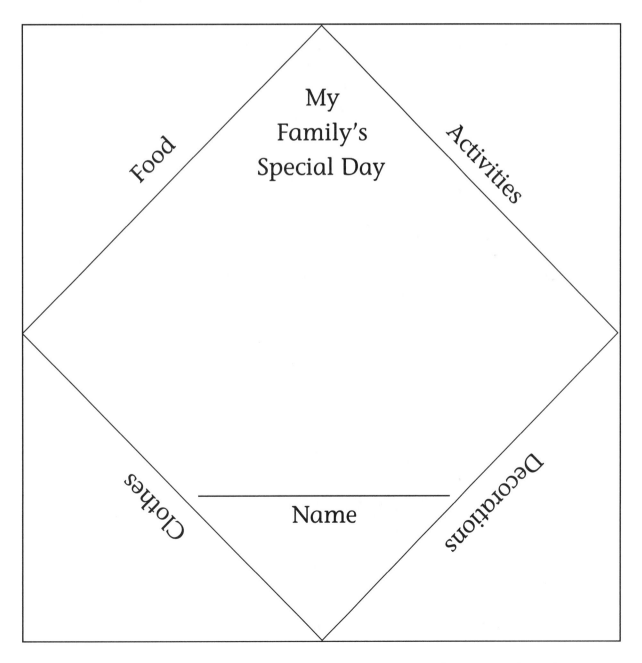

Chapter 13 Assessment

Big Ideas

Look at the pictures. Follow the directions below.

1. Find a birthday tradition from Mexico. Color it yellow.

2. Find a holiday tradition from China. Color it red.

Reading Further

3. Find a music tradition from Africa. Color it brown.

Show You Know

4. Think of a holiday. How does your family celebrate it?

   With words and pictures, answer these questions:

   - What is the holiday?

   - What decorations are there?

   - What foods do you eat?

   - What clothes do you wear?

   - What do you do?

Sample Puzzle

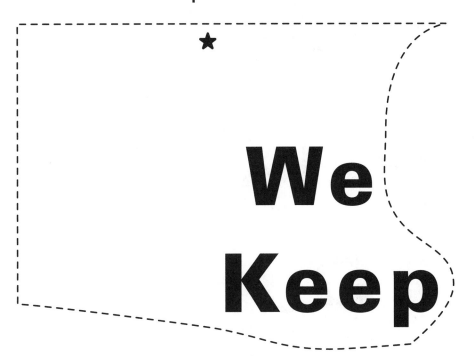

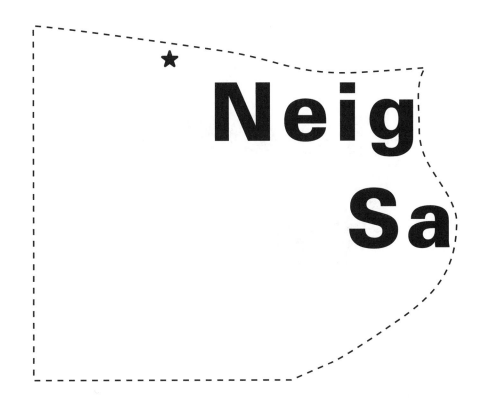

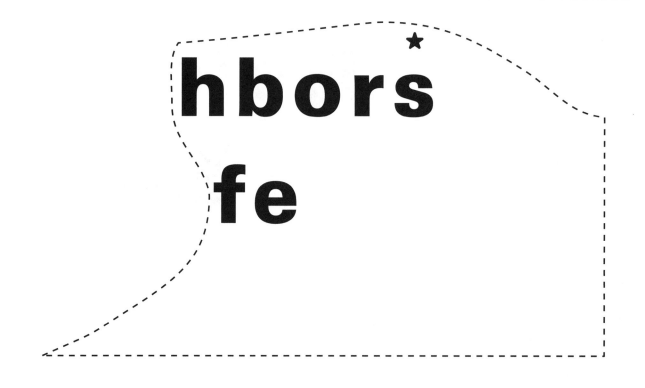

Roles for Your Group

Cutter 1

Cuts one page of the puzzle pieces in half.

Draws a picture on a puzzle piece.

Glues down one puzzle piece.

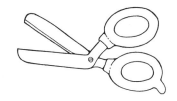

Cutter 2

Cuts the other page of the puzzle pieces in half.

Draws a picture on a puzzle piece.

Glues down one puzzle piece.

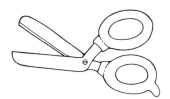

Checker

Draws a picture on a puzzle piece.

Checks that the puzzle is right before gluing.

Glues down one puzzle piece.

Presenter

Draws a picture on a puzzle piece.

Glues down one puzzle piece.

Shares the poster with the class.

Puzzle A

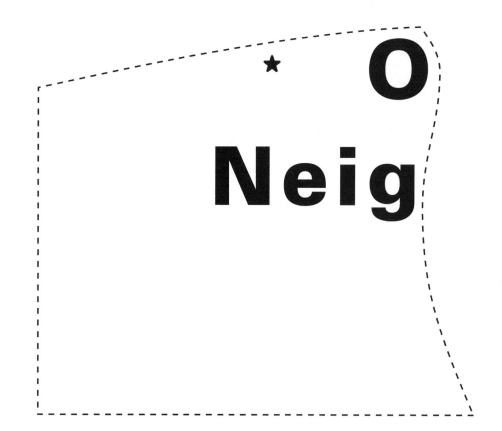

Help

**ur
hbors.**

Puzzle B

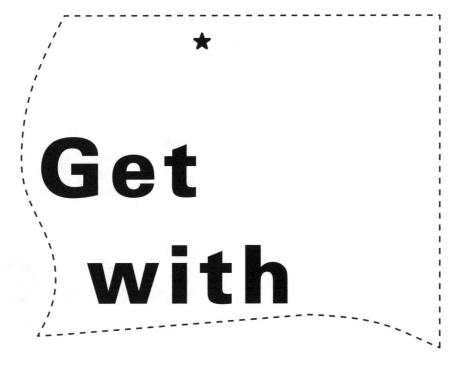

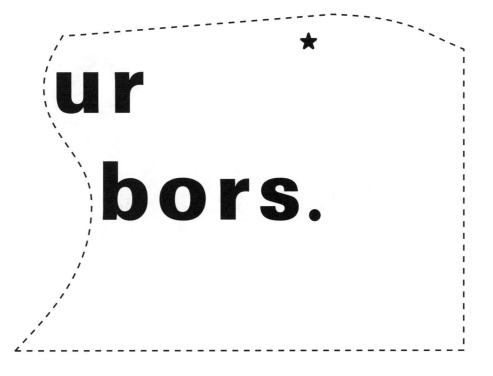

Puzzle C

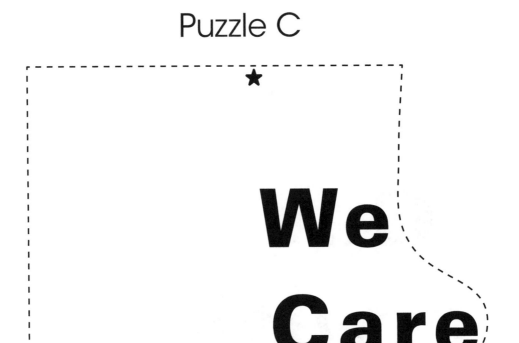

We
Care

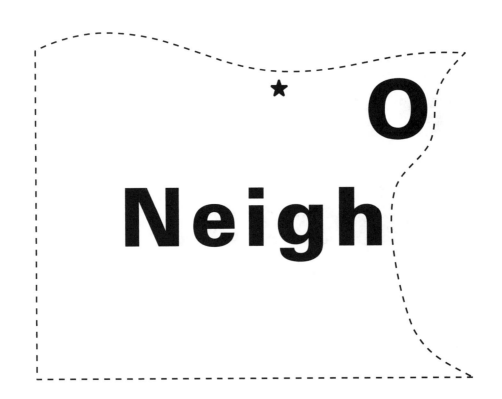

o
Neigh

Take of

ur borhood.

Story Cards

The woman met a neighbor who wanted a gift for his true love.

She traded the flowers for the man's puppy.

The woman met a pillow maker who had a garden.

The woman traded a bag of feathers for flowers.

Story Cards

A woman wanted to make an apple dumpling.

She headed down the road to trade a basket of plums.

The woman met a lonely neighbor with an apple tree.

She traded the puppy for apples.

Story Cards

The woman went home with her apples.

Now she could make an apple dumpling.

The woman met a neighbor with a flock of geese.

She traded her plums for a bag of feathers.

Chapter 14 Assessment

Big Ideas

How are these children being good neighbors?

Match each box to a sentence on the right. Draw lines.

1.

I keep our front yard looking nice.

We get along with our neighbors.

2.

I don't leave my toys where people might trip on them.

We take care of our neighborhood.

3.

I play with the little boy who lives next door.

We help keep our neighbors safe.

Reading Further

4. How did this woman get apples for her apple

   dumpling? Circle the best answer.

   A. She grew them.

   B. She traded for them.

   C. She bought them.

Show You Know

5. What is one way you are a good neighbor?

   • Draw a picture of yourself being a good neighbor.

   • Tell what makes you a good neighbor.

   I am a good neighbor because I _____

   _____.

Photographs

Front Cover
Ableimages/Getty Images

Title Page
Ableimages/Getty Images

Chapter 8
55 TL: ©2002 Stephanie Rausser-FPG/Getty Images **55 TR:** ©2002 Stephen Simpson-FPG/Getty Images **55 BL:** ©2002 AJA Productions-The Image Bank/Getty Images **55 BR:** ©2002 Arthur Tilley-FPG/Getty Images **56 TL:** ©2002 Romilly Lockyer-The Image Bank/Getty Images **56 TR:** ©2002 Michel Gounot-FPG/Getty Images **56 BL:** ©2002 Jeff Smith-The Image Bank/Getty Images **56 BR:** RF/Corbis **57 TL:** ©2002 Angelo Cavalli-The Image Bank/Getty Images **57 TR:** RF/Getty Images **57 BL:** ©2002 Jerry Kobalenko-Stone/Getty Images **57 BR:** RF/Getty Images

Chapter 9
66 L: Scott Bean **66 C:** Alantide Phototravel/Corbis **66 R:** George H. H. Huey/Corbis

Chapter 11
75 TL: Michele Westmorland/Getty Images **75 TR:** Ryan McVay/Getty Images **75 CL:** Steve Mason/Getty Images **75 CR:** Stephen Simpson/Getty Images **75 BL:** RF/Getty Images **75 BR:** Barbara Peacock/Getty Images

Chapter 12
88: George Marks/Getty Images

Art

Chapter 1
3: DJ Simison **4:** Doug Roy

Chapter 2
6: Doug Roy **8:** Doug Roy **9:** Doug Roy **10:** Doug Roy **11:** Jon Goodell

Chapter 3
13: Susan Jaekel

Chapter 4
19: Doug Roy **22:** Doug Roy
23 L: Gary Undercuffler **23 R:** Doug Roy
24 L: Gary Undercuffler **24 R:** Doug Roy
25 L: Gary Undercuffler **25 R:** Doug Roy
26 L: Gary Undercuffler **26 R:** Doug Roy
27 L: Gary Undercuffler **27 R:** Doug Roy
28 L: Gary Undercuffler **28 R:** Doug Roy
29 L: Gary Undercuffler **29 R:** Doug Roy
30 L: Gary Undercuffler **30 R:** Doug Roy
31 L: Gary Undercuffler **31 R:** Doug Roy
32 L: Gary Undercuffler **32 R:** Doug Roy
33 L: Gary Undercuffler **33 R:** Doug Roy
34 L: Gary Undercuffler **34 R:** Doug Roy
35: Gary Undercuffler

Chapter 5
37: Susan Jaekel **38:** Susan Jaekel **39:** Susan Jaekel **40:** Susan Jaekel **43:** Doug Roy **44:** DJ Simison

Chapter 6
49: Len Ebert

Chapter 7
51: Doug Roy **52:** Doug Roy **53:** Doug Roy

Chapter 8
59 T: Carol Newsome **59 C:** Carol Newsome **59 B:** Gary Undercuffler **60:** Doug Roy

Chapter 9
65: Gary Undercuffler

Chapter 10
70: Doug Roy **73:** Doug Roy **74:** Doug Roy

Credits

Chapter 11
79: Doug Roy **80:** Susan Jaekel **81:** Gary Undercuffler

Chapter 12
84: DJ Simison **86:** Doug Roy **87:** Gary Undercuffler

Chapter 13
95: Doug Roy **98:** Doug Roy

Chapter 14
103: Doug Roy **110:** Susan Jaekel
111: Susan Jaekel **112:** Susan Jaekel
113: Len Ebert **114:** Susan Jaekel

Artists represented by Ann Remen-Willis,
Artist Representative and Art Manager:

Len Ebert
Jon Goodell
Susan Jaekel
Carol Newsome
Doug Roy
DJ Simison
Gary Undercuffler